The Parkinali　Ɔetry Book

The Parkinality Poetry Book

*'Did you ask if you could
write a poem about my aunt?'*

and other poems

The Parkinality Poet

Matador
9 Priory Business Park,
Wistow Road, Kibworth Beauchamp,
Leicestershire. LE8 0RX
Tel: 0116 279 2299
Email: books@troubador.co.uk
Web: www.troubador.co.uk/matador
Twitter: @matadorbooks

ISBN 978 1838590 895

British Library Cataloguing in Publication Data.
A catalogue record for this book is available from the British Library.

Typeset in 10pt Georgia by Troubador Publishing Ltd, Leicester, UK

Matador is an imprint of Troubador Publishing Ltd

For... my mum and Louise.

Thank you to everyone
who has been there for me
here, there and everywhere,
especially e, c, h
and the wise(ish) man.

Contents

Deja vu: If some of these poems seem a little familiar, you may have heard me recite them at an open mic night. Or you may be one of the lucky one hundred people who purchased a limited edition "informal purple booklet" of some of my poems. The special editions were sold in aid of Parkinson's (PD) charities. Those poems (many now rewritten) are joined by new poems, also written by The Parkinality Poet, in this: *The Parkinality Poetry Book.*

'Did you ask if you could write a poem about my aunt?'

A poetry reader from Disgruntled-on-Sea writes:

Everything you've written rings true to me;
the poem even mentions halitosis and an urgency to wee.

My aunt wears the same slippers you describe in verse four;
so many similarities and I've just spotted some more.

Her sister's name is Kate, her dog's called Stan;
she never wed, never found the right man.

A canine-loving, single sister, who wears slippers all the time,
with a couple of hygiene issues, apart from that she's fine.

It must be my aunt, don't lie, it must be true;
if you've written a poem about Aunt Vera, then I want one too.

'I didn't write a poem about your Aunt Vera.'

The Parkinality Poet replies:

The poems are all original and fictional;
the people come from that busy place called... "My Imagination".
Any similarity to anyone/anything living or dead is purely
coincidental and completely unintentional.*
By the way, I realise these lines do not rhyme;
obviously, I don't converse in verse all of the time.

If you are suggesting that your aunt has some of the same traits,
as a lady in a poem I penned – that's a coincidence and a mistake.
The slippers were from a high street store – so not unique at all;
the names are also a coincidence: the dog was almost called Paul.

Smelly breath and wee are things your aunt would never discuss,
and you would never have noticed as she never made a fuss.
So we need to prove if the personal issues are really true,
as we move closer, I whisper to her, 'Do you need the loo?'

So, her breath doesn't smell and she doesn't have an urgency to wee;
I see that as conclusive proof – now do you believe me?
All the people are fictitious, whether in a rhyme or a song;
the poem isn't about your Aunt Vera – admit it, you were wrong.

---

* Very occasionally a poem might be based on someone, in which case I will make
that very clear.

The Parkinality Poet, aka Janet Bric-a-Brac, aka Julie Walker

www.parkinality.co.uk

Melvyn

Wembley

Announcing, 'Wembley, I love you,'
adrenaline surging through his veins;
Melvyn raises his arms upwards,
acknowledging the acclaim.

Winking at the pretty girls,
as they walk on by.
Older ladies blushing,
as they catch his eye.

Confident the audience love him,
as he packs his guitar away.
Seeing the same, familiar faces,
almost every single day.

Playing for love, not for money,
tunnels intensify the sound;
rock and roll can just be heard,
above the noise of the Underground.

Alice

It never rains

Outside yet inside – wet but dry,
constantly trying, to fathom out why,
it never rains, but always snows?
I don't believe we'll ever know.
Each day for her; it is the norm,
as she predicts, the perfect storm.

Standing, rigid and stock still,
staring straight ahead, until...
...the world upends, sky goes dark.
She feels the fear, until a spark...
...of light appears, the snow begins.
I can almost hear an angel sing.

Transcending time, snowflakes glide,
she feels the flakes fall inside.
Each day is a crisp winter's day;
snowflakes never lose their way.
Trapped, yet safe, in a glass dome;
the place which she calls her home.

Alice gazes at the globe,
enjoys the sight.
Will it snow?
She thinks it might.

Cath

Dust

Dust, dust, glorious dust,
dust is something you should *always* mistrust.
Extremely common, yet *extremely* clever,
easily removed with a stick and some feathers.

Hand Cath a fiver to make the dust leave;
she sprays on the polish, rolls up her sleeves.
Actually, that's sexist: "she" could be a "he",
but we know that it probably won't be.

A man is more likely to be watching football.
That's not a criticism; that's quite normal.
Men rarely dust, that is so true:
they simply have better things to do.

Dust is a commodity without a value.
When Cath dusts, does anyone say thank you?
At the end of the day, would you say,
'Great dusting Cath, you've achieved a lot today'?

Dust hides in the corners, waiting to strike,
which is usually in the middle of the night.
In the morning there's dust; goodness that's a bore.
Another day spent dusting would be a chore.

So, leave the dust, write on the table,
not with a pen, you "nar-na", your finger, if you're able.
Write "gone out on the town" and enjoy your life:
a clean and tidy house is a wasted life.

Anna

Bless you

Anna has everything a little girl could need,
including a unicorn,* and the cutest dog breed.
Anna has it all, plus a pink bouncy ball,
quite obviously spoilt, with no siblings at all.
She also has something money just can't buy.
'Anna has an allergy,' her mother will sigh.

Then: if you sneezed you were probably okay.
Now: dust or squirrels, which allergy is it today?
We drank from the garden hose, played out after school,
ate food off the floor, ignored the four-second rule.
Then: wipe your nose, go outside and play.
Now: take your anti-histamine once a day.

Today, we carry EpiPens and emergency lists;
this allergy influx, how did it come to this?
Did we get ill? Did we get stomach bugs?
Of course, and we were prescribed "lots of hugs".
This paranoia threatens to drive us mad.
Now run along, and wash *both* your hands.

---

*   PS. I know you are desperate to know how; her aunt simply put a horn on a cow.

Phil

Trolley dolly

'I've found something essential to life;
more useful than my useless ex-wife.'
'Crikey,' said Phil's mate, 'there's no need to shout.
Essential to life? What are you on about?'

'It never expects sympathy or a new dress;
doesn't care if I look a complete mess.
It's my silent assistant waiting in place,
unquestioning, without a look on its face.'

Phil slowly opens the door wide,
to reveal the delights he had placed inside.
On the shelf were his meat and two veg, kept piping hot,
until later that evening, when he planned to scoff the lot.

For Phil it really is the most perfect device,
it doesn't moan like his awful ex-wife.
The hostess trolley is ready at the flick of a switch;
and at the end of the night, doesn't expect a kiss.

Malcolm

99p

Lydia Smithers was the girl of my dreams;
she was beautiful and she sold ice creams.
'Cornet or cup,' she would simply say,
whilst whirling ice creams, in her wonderful way.

I stopped by the van, almost every day,
buying two ice creams, giving one away.
I went out of my way, by over a mile,
for a glimpse of Lydia's amazing smile.

The extra ice cream was for the small boy,
who was always there, clutching a toy.
He never had any money to pay,
always tearful, as the van drove away.

One day Lydia's dad took her to one side;
he had something to say, before he died.
'Look after the business, make me proud,
sell ice creams, play the music loud.'

After he passed away, come rain or shine,
Lydia still sold ice creams, but gave me mine.
No longer asking for money from me,
for the ice cream and flake, which were 99p.

When I asked Lydia, 'Why don't I pay?'
She reminded me of the day,
I came to the aid of her dad in the street,
when Parkinson's whipped him right off his feet.

Lydia said I was a lovely man,
for stopping and helping, beside the van,
where her dad sold ice creams, every day,
whilst others turned, and walked away.

Terrance

Paranoia

Shades on, head down, never catch their eye.
Stare at the pavement, never question why.
Sit on the tube, try to look calm.
Never trust a stranger, they might do you harm.
Never take a chance, never catch their eye.
Stare straight ahead, never question why.

Plug in, switch on, be together, but alone.
Hundreds of strangers on a mobile phone.
Work all day, alone, in our room.
Later play online, in the evening gloom.
We are in danger, of living in a virtual land,
where no-one ever shakes your hand.

What will become of the human race?
If we never again meet face to face?
Just a screensaver, with a log-in name.
Reality will become virtual;
life virtually a game.

Stanley

Alone or lonely

Anything for a quiet life,
anything at all.
Never making a fuss,
never crawling the walls.

On the periphery,
yet still in the room.
Please don't avoid,
please don't assume.

Looking around,
once in a while.
Hoping to catch,
somebody's smile.

No-one notices,
Stan is still there.
Sitting alone,
in his easy chair.

Lorraine and I

Dining Disaster

The word "drugs" conjures up images of crime,
Lorraine and I prefer to say "meds" at tablet time.
Pills attempt to keep symptoms at bay,
as Parkinson's tries to control our day.

We are constantly trying to avoid stress,
trying to inject some humour into this mess.
We seek an opportunity every day;
the ladies who lunch are our target today.

At a fancy lunch, we arrive quiet and calm,
until a lady tilts her head, touches my arm.
Then a mischievous idea occurs to me.
I scream, '*Give me my drugs!*'; Vi spits out her tea.

The ladies who lunch all stop, tut and stare;
gaining in confidence, we really don't care.
We stand and attempt to cross the room,
before our meds kick in, far too soon.

Lorraine staggers, shuffles and falls about,
'*I need more drugs now!*' I randomly shout.
Maud complains, Iris feels quite faint,
Vi once again spits tea onto her plate.

This amuses Lorraine and me for a while
and we both briefly break out into a smile.

Mel and Scott

Teamwork

Mel and Scott had worked long and hard,
re-working the famous plays of the Bard.
Four years in the making, seemed a lifetime;
the money had run out, time after time.
Preview tomorrow, everything just right;
all they needed was an early night.

Awaking refreshed, they had toast with jam,
the sun was shining, everything going to plan.
Mel hoped the cast remembered every song.
Scott was concerned that his trousers were too long.
The play finally began, after a slight delay;
No wrong words and Scott's trousers didn't fray.

The audience rose to their feet, during the final song,
gave a standing ovation, as they sang along.
Everyone loved the show, the reviews were great,
due to hard work, not due to fate.
Mel and Scott enjoyed their five minutes of fame;
they couldn't wait to do it all over again.

Mel and Scott were a brilliant team,
like footballers – do you know what I mean?
They always have their eyes on the ball;
teamwork is key, always giving their all.
At the end of the day, when their work is done
they walk home together; two become one.

Alfie

Under surveillance

"Constantly monitored", wherever he went.
"Under surveillance", whatever that meant.
Continuously watched from dusk 'til dawn,
twenty-four hours was the norm.
He was always accompanied, never alone,
even observed whilst on the phone.
Grateful he had his own chair and bed;
no cruelty: he was always well fed.

Now he needed freedom, he needed to speak,
plotting and scheming, for over a week.
Life needed to change, or he would go mad,
he was feeling quite frustrated and sad.
Tuesday at two, they were staring at him;
he raised his voice, above the din.
Despite his shouts, they couldn't understand;
they merely reached out, and took his hand.

Undeterred, he planned to try again,
needing to do something, or risk going insane.
Observing and learning, whenever he could,
watching and waiting, until he would.
He chose a moment, around midday;
she was looking the other way.
He glanced briefly, across the room;
this could not come a moment too soon.

Letting go of the table, he stretched his arms out,
his mother, Cath, began to shout,
his father, Dave, ran from the other room.
Alfie squealed – walking – not a moment too soon.

Stephanie

My constant...

Stephanie, with her tangled auburn hair,
sat quietly on her dressing table chair.
Her mummy gently combed the knots away,
making her hair pretty for her first school day.
Stephanie sat as straight as a bean;
she would be the smartest girl they had ever seen.

Stephanie wore her favourite dress in pale blue,
with black patent shoes, which were nearly new.
She walked proudly along Winchester Street,
wondering just who they might meet.
She loved her shoes, she loved her dress;
she loved being smart, and looking her best.

Her mummy kissed her on the forehead that day,
saying "I love you" in her own special way.
Stephanie clung to her mummy, held her hand.
Her mummy said, 'Be brave,' she did understand.
Saying she'd be back in an hour or so;
Stephanie watched her walk away, so slow.

Steph held her mum's hand and started to shout;
the needle went in, the needle came out.
She squirmed and kicked as it hit the spot;
Steph needed it, whether she liked it or not.
Without it, she could not survive:
that damn drug kept her alive.

Steph swallowed the pills, down they went,
straight from her mouth, to the main event,
entering her stomach, *en route* to her head.
Her mum sat patiently next to her bed.
Steph's existence, ruled by the pills,
which really do not cure all ills.

Her mum kissed her on the forehead that day,
saying "I love you" in her own special way.
Steph clung to her mum, held her hand.
Her mum said, 'Be brave,' she did understand.
Saying she'd be back in an hour or so;
Steph watched her walk away, so slow.

Many years have passed, yet so little time,
her mum, her constant, her daughter's lifeline.
At nursery school, her mummy was back at two;
twenty years on, her mum returns promptly too.
Both times reaching out, their hands entwine,
feeling safe, until the next time.

Lucy

Number thirty-nine

Lucy wrote her bucket list in nineteen eighty-nine;
today, she had reached number thirty-nine.
Number thirty-nine was composing a song;
she was confident it wouldn't take her very long.
How hard could it really actually be?
If musicians could do it, then so could she.

The song must have rhythm, and a good beat,
Lucy loved to dance, with her two left feet.
She was finding it hard to choose an original theme;
her ideas were odd – you'll soon see what I mean.
Squirrels, cress and tiny pieces of cheese;
if you have any suggestions, help her please.

After working all day, it was getting rather late;
Lucy needed to get ready for a blind date.
Stereo on, selecting her dress,
Applying lipstick, wanting to look her best.
The song would have to wait for another day;
grabbing her coat, she went on her way.

At first the date was good, they got along great;
he was a songwriter, it must have been fate.
Looking into her eyes, he wrote her a song;
it really didn't take him very long.
Lucy was intrigued, she wasn't going to lie;
he told her every tune should say "influenced by".

Later, he said goodbye at her front door;
Lucy was relieved, he had actually been such a bore.
She still had the lyrics, the night hadn't been in vain.
she quickly changed the odd word, added her name.
No qualms at all, it was only a tiny white lie;
well, every song should say "influenced by".

Bill

Stuff

Working all the hours, fingers to the bone,
you must have the latest mobile phone.
She must have the watch and designer dress;
the house and car must be the best.

Will stuff make you happy, do you really believe it will?
Before you answer, I suggest you visit Bill.
Bill lives round the corner in the next street;
he's one of the happiest people you'll ever meet.

Bill wears a smile, always says hello;
ask him about his stuff, I know you want to know.
He has every type of gadget, every type of tool;
"Look but don't touch", is Bill's unwritten rule.

Bill was just like you and me,
until he left that life in 2003.
He had to leave, just turn and go;
they never asked why, they didn't want to know.

Today Bill is skint, but still has stuff like you.
Is he honest or a thief? Let me give you a clue.
You earn the money, you get the stress;
Bill sifts through your rubbish, selects from your mess.

Today Bill sits in the sun, you still push that pen.
Bill has version nine, you have version ten.
Buy today's gadget, throw yesterday's away,
upgraded with a new button, which you won't use anyway.

John

Part One

John left the cottage, never to return;
as he walked down the path, the fire started to burn.
No-one saw, no-one heard.
Did he phone the brigade? Don't be absurd.

John chose the place where the fire was lit:
the window seat, where she loved to sit.
He didn't turn back, he didn't look round;
John was certainly not feeling proud.
Starting the fire, which would probably end,
the life of his wife, his dearest friend.

Claire awoke, hearing the front door slam,
looking out of the window, she saw her old man.
Pulling on her robe, she ran from the room,
before the fire took hold, not a moment too soon.
She stood watching the brigade extinguish the flame,
not realising that her husband was to blame.

John should have waited, he really should,
instead he ran, as fast as he could.
Faster and faster, he ran through the town,
and onto the track; the express ran him down.

Claire
Part Two

The post-mortem was a challenge to do:
forensics spent days gathering clues.
It was a waste of time, as there was no doubt,
when a train strikes, it gives quite a clout.

Claire and John's marriage hadn't been quite the same,
since he was sacked, although he wasn't to blame.
Claire felt the pressure, she was under so much strain;
she couldn't afford to be made redundant again.
Ten years of married life, ten years of joy;
so why did trust walk out the door?

Every single night Claire worked until late,
when John thought she was on an illicit date.
Claire also convinced – John was having an affair.
They both tried so very hard, not to care.
No evidence, but both thought they knew.
Unaware their "sixth sense" was slightly askew.

Each so busy, wrapped up in their own life,
they had stopped living as husband and wife.
They should have talked, the signs were misread;
now it was too late, now one of them was dead.

Natalie

Thank you

Always a smile, hardly a frown,
even though, some days, must get her down.

Never fussing, just efficiently here,
plumping up pillows, whilst lending an ear.

Press the button, the bell calls her in,
obs, meds, bed pans, could be anything.

Constantly here for you, always on call,
day or night, it doesn't matter at all.

Caring for, every single person here,
each day helping, to alleviate fear.

She mops your brow, feels your pain,
the next day, she will return again.

Damon

Alien invasion

Intrigued by a small ad in the local rag,
forty men set off, each wearing a bum-bag.
The advert was cryptic, not giving much away;
bring: a spade, a doily and a bale of hay.
An odd list, but they did as they were told;
they were a strange group – all seventy-five years old.
Thirty-eight Scorpios, a couple of Pisces too.
No-one knew what they would be asked to do.

They gathered at midnight just outside Tring,
where a huge spaceship stood silently waiting.
An alien emerged and surveyed the crowd,
as the dishevelled group gathered round.
Antennas twitching, he selected just one;
Damon was excited, his adventure had finally begun.
Clutching a spade in his hand and a doily made of lace,
he ran, scattering hay, with a smile on his face.

The door shut, as Damon boarded the ship;
he loved the decor, it was surprisingly hip.
The furnishings eclectic, the music niche;
Damon and the alien chatted, whilst nibbling quiche.
As they danced 'til dawn on that moonlit night,
Damon was loving the vibe but, try as he might,
he just couldn't relax, couldn't calm down;
he was still wearing his Parkinson's frown.

Suddenly Damon awoke rigid, unable to turn,
his body in spasm, dystonia began to return.
It started in his feet, his back and his neck;
desperate for some relief: 'Oh flaming heck.'
Damon was sad to leave his amazing dream,
where everything wasn't as it had seemed.
Where aliens existed, where Damon was free,
and it wasn't all about disease and sodding PD.

Margaret

Electronic cake

It's wasting my time, driving me up the wall,
this so-called "useful tool".
It has completely taken over my life,
just switching it on causes me strife.

I need a computer to type, play music too;
to find the Longomontanus, as I don't have a clue.
Addicted to information, the machine draws me in,
volumes of encyclopaedias consigned to the bin.

Will it mess with my mind, if I stare at it all day?
Will it addle kids' brains? Just go outside and play.
How long before the computer is cited in a divorce?
'More interesting than the wife? Well, of course.'

Rather than meet up, we type a few short strokes,
rather than chat, we simply emote.
Not sure how I would react or what I would do,
if you messaged me a smiling pile of poo.

What will become of the human race,
if we never again meet face to face?
I'd rather meet for a cuppa, that's not fake.
Remember – you can't eat electronic chocolate cake.

Judith

Harmless fun?

He got away with it every time,
repeating the same old crime,
"Blow to the head", on the report.
"An accident", his usual retort.

What had made him commit this awful act?
He couldn't deny it; it was a statement of fact.
Each time the policeman asked him, 'Why?'
Under cross examination, told not to lie.

He simply hung his head in shame,
promising never to do it again.
Each day Judith hoped he would change,
but each day he became more deranged.

It was a wicked thing to do,
in front of all those kids too.
Striking his wife, hit after hit,
chanting, 'That's the way to do it.'

As the sun set on this nostalgic scene,
families reflected on what they had seen.
Mums downed the wine they had smuggled in,
leaving dads to explain what Punch did was a sin.

Samantha

Deception

Planning was vital; that's what she'd read.
Preparation was needed for the task ahead.
Discussing with others, consulting a book;
it was extremely important, how it looked.

They must be hidden, never seen;
disguise was key, you'll soon see what I mean.
She hated deception, she was honest, you see,
but she had no choice, he *must* eat his greens.

Peas and broccoli were secreted away,
to ensure Bartholomew consumed five a day.
Deception was the name of the game.
A healthy toddler, the ultimate aim.

Joanna

Commuter companion

Joanna, thirty-two, was a single lady,
who commuted into London daily.
By day, she worked hard as the head of PR.
By night, she adjourned to the local bar.

There city types would give a cheeky wink;
occasionally she would accept just one drink.
A quick drink and a friendly chat;
surely there was nothing wrong with that?

The shoulder she gave them was definitely cold;
they were often too rich, or far too old.
She enjoyed the attention, despite the same old lines,
until the mood changed, which happened each time.

The mood changed as the rug was swept away,
which happened to Joanna virtually every day.
'Maybe see you later,' the city types walked away,
as Parkinson's, again, disrupted Joanna's day.

Margery

Love it or loathe it

Should it stay?
Should it go?
Does anybody really know?

Like it there?
Leave it be?
It really is nothing to do with me.

Not sure why some hate the sight.
Some feel strongly, get quite uptight.

Just mind your own business,
simply let it go.

Stay *au natural*,
simply let it grow.

Honestly, no-one will really care.
If you decide to keep your underarm hair.

Deirdre
Really?!

What have you done? You really don't know?
Why did I send you? I'd have been happy to go.
You had choices, you had enough money;
don't look at me like that, it really isn't funny.

I'm usually not that fussy. I really am not;
own brand would have been fine, I'm not a snob.
I asked you nicely, I even said please.
So why did you buy the stuff that you squeeze?

As bad, would have been triangles and strings;
who actually buys those awful things?
Something else which fills me with dread,
are pre-sliced squares, on sliced white bread.

Actually, you must also avoid the diet shelf;
it simply shouldn't be good for your health.
Mould and fat are part of its charm;
don't worry, it won't do you any harm.

Traditionally made forwards (I'm sure you know),
try it "madE" backwards – go on, give it a go.
You don't have to go to an artisan deli,
or buy the fancy stuff, advertised on the telly.

Crackers or bread, either is fine,
as long as I have a nice glass of wine.
I'm not high maintenance, I'm easy to please,
as long as you buy me the right cheese.

Sue

Overdue books

Justin and Sue moved into their new abode;
Tracey and Tony lived over the road.
Joanna lived just next door but one;
on the corner: Dave, Cath and Alfie, their son.

Sue was excited about this new phase of her life;
she really wanted to be a good wife,
a mother, a lover and a cook.
She had read all about it in a library book.

About how to keep a man happy so he didn't stray.
Sue wanted him to love her in every way.
She set about learning to cook and to sew,
gaining every skill a good wife should know.

Justin worked hard, as good husbands do.
Sue tidied, ironed and cleaned the loo,
and scrubbed the floors until they shone.
Trying to ensure she did nothing wrong.

Justin and Sue met in the local pub,
which really was a stroke of luck.
If Sue had been earlier and Justin late,
they wouldn't have met; their meeting was fate.

When Justin saw Sue, it was love at first sight,
but when Sue saw Justin – try as she might,
it wasn't love at first sight, but to be fair,
Sue tried to love him; she tried to care.

Six months of marriage, they muddled along,
trying to be happy, trying to get along.
Justin did all he could think of for Sue;
he really wanted her to love him too.

On the day of the divorce, Justin cried.
On the day of the divorce, Sue... lied.
Justin walked away, lost and distraught.
Sue went home, drank more than she ought.

Sue brushed herself down, got on with her life,
with husband number – eight – she would be a good wife,
a mother, a lover and a cook.
She had read all about it in a library book.

Nancy

Creating confusion

Nancy wore thigh-high boots in baby pink,
she had a sexy walk and a flirty wink.
She was different from the usual staff.
Did the guys like her? 'Cor not 'arf.'
Dan wasn't sure if it was her sparkling wit,
or the size of her... smile.

She was never early, always late,
but stayed longer, until after eight.
Nancy worked hard, but didn't do much,
Well-educated, but Dan had a hunch.
Nancy seemed too good to be true.
Dan took her to lunch to gain some clues.

He'd heard a rumour, something she hadn't told us,
Dan said, 'I'm not prying; I don't want a fuss.
I've heard a few rumours about you,'
as he stared into her eyes, which were baby blue.
'I need to ask, before we take you on:
is your name Nancy, or is it really John?'

Dan wasn't prepared for what happened next;
tears ran down Nancy's face, she bit her lip.
She launched the water, including the glass,
straight at his back, drenching his arse.
Nancy turned and flounced from the room.
Flip – she wasn't usually found out so soon.

Tracey and Tony

Live for today

Tracey and Tony worked hard at their life;
he loved her, his darling trouble and strife.
They wanted for nothing, but didn't have much,
relying on each other, using each as a crutch.
Supporting each other through the austerity years;
coping, surviving, working through their fears.

The life they wanted was a life full of hope:
children, a dog and a house in "South Oak".
A very different place from where they began,
in a terraced house with a beat-up white van.
They knew they could do it, working night and day,
to turn their plans into their reality.

They never went out, they saved every penny;
a night out was a night in, in front of the telly.
They made sacrifices, they dug their heels in,
saving for the future, when their life would begin.
A planner on the wall, mapping out the way;
they would save for tomorrow, not live for today.

No-one suggested they detour from this route,
except Nora, Tony's Gran, who was very astute.
She gave them advice, they pushed her away,
ignoring her words, saying, 'Please live for today.'
She was older and wiser than Tracey and Tone,
but all they saw was an interfering old crone.

Working too hard, their life put on hold;
when they should have been living, they wouldn't be told.
The date their lives changed was in September:
a doctor's words; it was a day they'd always remember.
They'd been happy before, don't get me wrong,
but wished they'd lived more, before Parkinson's came along.

Sara

Remember when?

Sara was content to sit quietly all day;
she was actually happier that way.
Preferable to the bustle and rush,
and the noise, she preferred the hush.

She sat and thought, calmly, she did.
Thinking about the time John was a kid,
Suzanna was a child, and David was a baby.
Was that long ago? She wanted to say, 'Maybe.'

To Sara "long ago" was only the other day,
when John was stung by a bee, Suzanna ran away.
David cried so much we thought he would burst;
he drank his milk; it quenched his thirst.

Strangers came to visit and hold Sara's hand;
they talked about things she didn't understand.
About Alfie, Cath and Dave as well.
She was interested but had no time to dwell.

Sara looked around the room, confused.
She didn't understand; she was bemused.
Where was he? He was never late,
Sara needed to see him – her soulmate.

Waiting – is what she did every day.
Today was important: it was their birthday.
Michael passed away in two thousand and five,
but to Sara he was still alive.

Lola

Undercover plumber

Nails attach new taps to each shoe.
What on earth is Lola up to?

Lola attempts a ball change, a step after that,
adding a skip and a hop, adjusting the tilt of her hat.
Getting into the rhythm, really feeling the beat,
as the music begins to take over her feet.

Souls combine as they move as one;
mind and feet begin to get along.
Connections made, her body moves in time,
as Lola's arms join this musical mime.

Steps are repeated, counting each move;
Lola relaxes, gets into the groove.
Her shoes start to find their voice;
they choose the sound, she has no choice.

Shuffle, hop, tap, step, ball change, a step in time;
stop, repeat, continue, she feels sublime.
Amazed and excited, she never wants this to end;
dance is Lola's new best friend.

Dave

Confidence

Dave knows the odds;
he has the stake.
Now let him take a chance.

The ball is dropped;
it hits the spot,
and glistens in the light.

It jumps and hops,
and hops and jumps.
Will it stop? It might.

Well, of course it will,
it's not alive;
it's not a living thing.
Eventually, it will cease to move,
and notes go in the bin.

The ball lands on red,
or is that black?
He'll always take a chance.
Which number has it settled on?
He gives a second glance.

Black number four or number two?
He really doesn't care.
He is feeling confident,
as he pulls up a chair.

An hour passes, or is that two?
The day turns to night,
as the tiny ball continues,
its evening flight.

Hopping and jumping its way,
around the spinning wheel.
Will it change his life?
He thinks it probably will.

Dave is confident things will be okay,
especially if he's here, every single day.
He walks away; it's been a busy night.
He decides to take the bus home tonight.

Gill

Retail sheep

Sampson's was always Gill's favourite store,
after J&T's, which was next door.
Sampson's for frocks, J&T's for smalls,
preferable to impersonal shopping malls.

"Shop 'til you drop" was always her philosophy,
after which she would go for afternoon tea.
First in the queue for the January sales,
first to view Christmas window displays.

Today Sampson's is still Gill's favourite store,
after J&T's, which is still next door.
In fact, you could say Sampson's is now her home.
although she won't be installing a telephone.

As temperatures fall, she wears the layered look,
found in the bins, not the Designers' Look Book.
Life had been complicated, life is simpler today;
no need to lock a cardboard box at the end of each day.

All she asks is that when she settles down to sleep,
she doesn't have to count too many sheep.

Ross

Love me, love me not

Ross needed her,
right from the start.
Gazing into her eyes,
seeing into her heart.

He watched as she sat,
and thought awhile.
All he wanted,
was to see her smile.

He loved her,
and hoped she might.
He took her hand,
squeezing it tight.

Feeling her breath,
he touched her hair.
Whispered, 'I love you,'
he really did care.

She turned away,
and faced the sun.
Smiling, she knew:
he was the one.

Gloria and Mitchell
Paint that town

'Give me my drugs,' Gloria Flambard demands.
'Give me drugs, now,' sounding quite unkind.
No please or thank you passes her lips,
just a wink of her eye, and a swish of her hips.
That is where the sass and confidence ends,
as she grabs the arm of Mitchell Benn.

Mitchell says, with a soft, calming voice,
'Be patient my darling, you do have a choice.
You are a lady, not a coarse youth;
rudeness and shouting, are very uncouth.
Be calm, my dear, it's really not that bad.'
Mitchell Benn reaches out to take her hand.

Gloria pushes him away, full of despair.
Mitchell may love her, he really may care,
but how could he possibly understand?
She needs drugs now, not to hold his hand.
Gloria looks away, to avoid his gaze;
she has tried to explain in so many ways.

It's easy to understand: the physicality,
the tremor and shuffle, are plain to see.
It's the invisible symptoms inside her brain,
which are draining and hard to explain.
Depression, apathy, insomnia – oh hell!
So many symptoms, she must be unwell.

Parkinson's is trying to break her from within,
but Gloria is determined it will never win.
She really doesn't mean to make a fuss,
just wanting to be normal and one of us.
Gloria can't make Parkinson's go away,
but she prays a cure is found one day.

Gloria and Mitchell plan to spend the rest of their life,
living in sin, not as husband and wife.
That would be humdrum and run of the mill,
and they certainly weren't, before Gloria became ill.
Rest assured, they're not waiting to drop dead;
they will continue to go and paint the town red!

Jack

Boxer

Shuffling and staggering into the ring,
haven't touched a drop of gin.
Bantam, feather, heavy or light?
Are we talking chickens? No, having a fight.

Standing, staring with a blank look,
left foot forward, prepare a right hook.
Jack's not here to try and win,
holding his gloves close to his chin.

Jab, punch, hit or blow,
above the belt, never below.
Jab, cross, left hook and repeat,
standing, feeling light on his feet.

Pads are the target, not the face,
starting to quicken up the pace.
Repeating, time and time again,
not intending to cause any pain.

Turn around, make a lunge,
grab hold of the magic sponge.
Mop away those beads of sweat,
still going strong, not done yet.

Movements really start to flow;
as he punches, who would know?
The power surprises him,
starting to feel that he could win.

Never a knock out.
Never down and out.
No final countdown.
Never out for the count.

Confidence really starts to grow,
Jack will take you on, have a go.
Ding ding – flip – it was going so well.
You were lucky, saved by the bell.

Leonard
White collar worker

Popular with both women and men,
the service he offered, was unique to him.
People were fickle, he knew that was true,
but he'd always be there for each one of you.

Most days he'd perform, to a small crowd.
On holidays, he had to shout, quite loud,
to get over the "delightful" din of girls and boys,
playing with the second-hand toys.

Women would approach to his front door,
to talk of marriage to the man they adored.
He blessed their babies, on their Christening days,
said a short prayer, then went on his way.

Births, marriages, deaths: all pivotal days,
chatting about old times, how things had changed.
Exchanging stories, a joke with your mate,
planning to keep in touch, before it's too late.

However, most of the time the vicar was left,
with one core group, but he wasn't bereft.
He knew everyone worshipped every day,
but not necessarily in the biblical way.

Jennifer

All dressed up...

Strawberry, platinum, mouse or ash?
Too many choices, too little cash.
Foils, roots, t-section or cap?
Wearing a gown, looking crap.

Bronzer, lipstick, a little blush,
so many layers, Jen's in a rush.
Contouring, highlights defining her face,
making her look less of a disgrace.

Blouse, jumper, dress or shirt?
Mini, midi, slacks or skirt?
Blue, orange, pink or green?
She doesn't want to look too keen.

Jennifer knows just where to wait.
Expectations low, not expecting a date.
Silently waiting, hoping to catch his eye,
but he didn't look round, he just walked on by.

She waited an hour near his office door,
hoping he'd walk past once more.
So that she'd have a chance again that day,
of glimpsing his back, as he walked away.

Kev

Tortoise and the hare

Heart racing, though his chest,
Kev needs to win, to be the best.
'This race is crucial, can't you see?
I'm determined you won't outrace me.'

Both hold their breath, poised and keen,
on the grid, waiting for green.
Kev leads from the front, not letting her in;
second's not an option, he's here to win.

They approach the corner, the end is in sight.
She loses the back end, try as she might.
Losing control, her car leaves the track,
rolls in the air, lands on its back.

No marshal comes running.
No fire brigade called.
No ambulance forthcoming.
Don't look appalled.

Back on the track, back in the groove,
she nudges the car; it starts to move.
Squeezing the throttle, gaining speed,
approaching the hairpin, it's a win that she needs.

Fingers stiff,
Knees in pain.
Never give in.
No pain, no gain.

Kev's race was perfect, he expected a win that night,
no need for headlights, just the living room light.
Taking the final straight, the cat pounced, disrupting Kev's race,
and his sister overtook, winning, with a smile on her face.

Phyllis and Alfred

Compatible?

Phyllis Petunia Gladys Millway,
looked fabulous, as she sassed away.
She was the perfect woman – I'm sure you'd agree:
tall, beautiful and wonderfully happy.

Phyllis loved blue, that was plain to see;
she wore it from her head to her knee.
Never yellow or pink, always blue,
in many different tones and hues.

Phyllis was like the Queen, formal and smart.
She was posh like the Queen, but she did like to fart.

Alfred Michael Veronica Conway,
looked fabulous, as he sassed away.
He was the perfect man – I'm sure you'd agree:
tall, handsome and wonderfully happy.

Alfred loved green, that was plain to see,
he wore it from his head to his knee.
Never grey or brown, always green,
in many different shades he was seen.

Alfred was like the King, formal and smart,
He was posh like the King, but he did like to fart.

Alfred and Phyllis had led interesting lives:
Phyllis four husbands, Alfred three wives.
In the twilight years, they were alone, but not lonely;
each would love to meet their "one and only".

They were a perfect match, I saw them each day,
separately walking down Warblers Way.
Then last week Phyllis was early and Alfred late;
I held my breath, this must be fate.

Alfred was striding like only a real man would,
Phyllis teetered on heels, carefully as she could.
Would they finally meet... was there a chance?
But they walked on by, without a second glance.

Why, when they seemed so perfect in every way?
Then, of course, I realised the other day.
It would never have worked, no matter how keen:
"together, blue and green should never be seen".

Tamara
Enhancing perfection

'Enhancing perfection isn't against the law,'
announced Tamara, Botox "enhancing" her jaw.
Size zero? Possibly, she was certainly stick-thin.
Designer label? More likely, the bargain bin.

Tamara, thirty-two, wearing favourite attire,
was nearer to forty, and a little liar.
She had used every trick, in every book,
taken every tip, tried every look.

Her dates were like cups of tea,
beginning hot; she was flirty,
then gradually cooling, as time went by,
constantly searching for the perfect guy.

At forty, she decided to start a new life,
giving up on ever becoming a wife.
So, Tamara used a man; he had his fun.
She didn't want a father, just to be a mum.

The birth stretched her, in more ways than one.
As she pushed, she prayed it wasn't a son.
Tamara's life began again in that hospital bed,
her daughter's warmth, the scent of her head.

Tamara loved Sophie, more and more each day,
as she grew into make-up and out of play.
Beautiful gowns and curled hair,
Tamara believed money would show she cared.

In her teens, Sophie shunned material goods,
guilty of growing up, never up to no good.
Tamara, unfazed, loved the tattoo on Sophie's arm.
"Self-expression doesn't cause any harm".

Sophie announced, at twenty-one,
'I've booked the op,' to become her mother's son.
Her mum was not upset; she was in awe,
'Enhancing perfection isn't against the law.'

Nora

Knit one

Knit one, purl one – or is that three?
A nice pair of bed socks for your granny.
A scarf for Tracey; a jumper for Tone.
Wool, needles... and away we go.

Nora was delighted: the Vicar asked her to knit,
a huge ark, with all the animals in it.
She had the pattern, wool and knew what to do,
but knitted one of each animal, when Noah wanted two.

She said to duplicate and make two of each was silly:
knitted animals can't procreate – they don't have a willy.
The animals arrived at the ark in pairs that rainy day,
although not as married couples, she preferred it that way.

A much better idea was to bring friends together,
including reptiles with scales and birds with feathers.
An aardvark was friendly with an ant.
A lion with a sheep, and a dog with a cat.

Granny Nora just wanted to fill the world with joy,
where everyone held hands: every girl, every boy.
No fighting between species, no telling lies,
no shouting at the elephants, 'Who ate all the pies?'

Tony and Tracey visited on a beautiful spring day.
They hoped it was there; they really did pray.
The ark was on display in church on the 15th of May,
which would have been Granny's 100th birthday.

Ralph
Clipboard

I am in charge; listen to me now.
The work has to be done – I don't care how.
Health and safety is necessary, those are the rules.
In my day it didn't exist; in my day we had balls.

In my day, we had none of this paper work;
just a plaster on your thumb, if you got hurt.
Who cared if the ladder was wobbly, bricks too big?
Overtime forms? Just bunged you fifty quid.

The boss with the clipboard, and the string-attached pen,
wandering about, shouting orders at the men.
The clipboard makes him appear distant and talk crap,
hiding behind it, peering through the gap.

Give a man a clipboard and he thinks he's in charge;
this happened to Ralph – he was giving it large.
He held the clipboard like a comfort toy,
just like Harold the elephant, when he was a boy.

Ralph went home to an empty house each night.
Then last Tuesday he thought he might,
invite the lads for a drink at the local pub,
then onto the Tandoori for some Indian grub.

But the lads said "no" and walked away,
even though they were going to the Indian anyway,
to meet up with mates from the other building site,
and their boss, Steve, they went out each night.

Ralph with the clipboard in front of his face,
was a decent bloke, but he looked two-faced.
Steve had his hands free, he worked with the men;
he kept his pencil behind his ear, he was still one of them.

Maurice

Exhaustion

Maurice, with a black moustache, curly white hair,
was extremely short, suave and debonair.
In ten years, he'll be ninety-five years old,
living the high life, since investing in gold.

He'd travelled through every country in the land,
(well, the ones from which he hadn't been banned).
He'd had every job, from a builder to a thief.
Oh yes, and he still had all his own teeth.

Maurice had felt loved all of his life,
as a child, and by every single wife.
He grabbed each moment, lived life to the full.
In a china shop, he was the bull.

Today, he has hung up his little black book,
shredding it, so he couldn't sneak a final look.
His life had been full of good times and strife.
Maurice, exhausted, needed rest from his life.

Janet

Don't judge

Janet loves life, she lives for today,
grabbing opportunities as they come her way.
Always up for a challenge, always up for fun,
each night dreaming of things still to be done.

On the outside, she's Janet, always trying to win,
but something disruptive lurks within.
Six years ago, an uninvited guest,
took over her life, but at whose request?

Janet never knows what Parkinson's is going to do.
Will she be able to walk when she needs the loo?
Yes, this simple worry is one of many, you see,
which occupy Janet's mind (enough of her wee).

One minute frozen, the next she is thawed.
Sorry, a lot of you may now be bored,
with Janet harping on about life with this thing;
well then, unsubscribe and watch her dancing.

Whilst you watch, think to yourself,
Parkinson's is not so bad, she is not on the shelf.
But the real PD, hides underneath.
Is Janet smiling, or baring her teeth?

Janet asks that you stop and think today.
How would you feel if PD came your way?
Would you worry about going out, being seen,
or go out, dance and produce some dopamine?

Sheila

Beauty is in the eye...

Brazil nut? More English rose.
A week in the sun equals one red nose.
Is fake bake, the answer to my prayer?
"American Tan"? I really don't care.

Padding, enhancing; a fillet or a sock?
Check in the mirror, to avoid a shock,
when you're dancing and people see,
suddenly your boobs are around your knees.

False bits lost whilst swimming in the sea;
are there eyelashes on the beaches of Italy?
Stranded false nails, extensions in your hair,
lost property really is an international affair.

If you could buy person pieces in the town,
smooth out crow's feet, remove the frowns.
Everyone would look exactly the same,
which would be boring and a real shame.

Plastic surgery fills me with fear,
inevitably painful, and extremely dear.
People's quirkiness and unique features,
make human beings interesting creatures.

If you look in the mirror, feel a mess,
enhance your good bits with a new shirt or dress.
Save your money, don't risk your health,
stay *au natural*, and you won't be on the shelf.

Tina

Launderette

Today is two years since Raymond went away,
when he broke her heart, on that summer's day.
Why did he go? Tina still didn't know.
The note simply said, "Sorry, I have to go".

Every weekday, Tina would fold;
it was quite a skill, she'd been told,
to neatly press the clothes each day,
at the launderette, on Windowpane Way.

She arrived at eight, left at seven;
Tina spent her day, in ironing heaven.
Up to her ears in creased attire,
until the day when she would retire.

Whilst she folded, she would ponder.
Staring out of the window, she would wonder.
Standing and thinking about a time,
when she was happy and life was divine.

They met each day by the factory gate,
strolling together (he was usually late).
Holding hands, spending the walk,
exchanging news – goodness they could talk.

They fell in love, over the Summer of '71;
she was so happy: she knew he was the one.
'Those were the days,' she would sigh.
'When we were "us", you and I.'

Tina gazed out of the window today,
still wondering why he went away.
As she wiped away her usual tears,
a familiar soft voice whispered in her ear.

'I should've never gone away,
I've thought about you every day.'
As Raymond gathered her in his arms again,
she knew their love would never wane.

John Smith and John Smith

Midnight makeover

John Smith and John Smith have the same name,
but have never met, which is a shame.
Both working in an office, from eight-thirty 'til five;
they both hate it, but it keeps them alive.

John and John both meander through life,
not wanting, or looking for a wife.
The grannies say, 'It's a shame to miss out.'
'But we don't like women,' they politely point out.

If only they'd looked up whilst on the commuter train,
both travelling on the 06:56 time and time again.
Their eyes might have met, a spark might have been seen.
A connection made – you know what I mean.

Then they might have found love on the London express,
even though at 7am, they didn't always look their best.
It was at midnight they became "fabulous darling",
transformed from John and John, into Nancy and Marlene.

Colin and Veronica

Odd couple

Colin and Veronica have never met:
he lives in Oxford, she resides in Kent.
He likes snow, she loves the sun.
He votes Labour, she votes for the other one.

Lab coat over civvies is Colin's usual attire,
and goggles, not wasting time with a tie.
Veronica always polite, incredibly smart,
obligatory pearls, she looks the part.

Colin works, focusing his mind,
on finding a cure... which he *will* find.
Never wasting money, spending it well;
his job is vital, he knows that too well.

Colin has bunsen burners, Veronica her fundraising team.
Working in a lab, raising funds – never met, never seen.
Colin is aware, of the power he holds,
but he doesn't need to keep being told.

Colin doesn't know when there will be a cure, he can't lie,
until then he stops people wanting to die.

Nick

Wait in line

People gathered from near and far,
including a guy from the local bar;
a lad who milked cows at the dairy farm;
and a lady who was odd, but meant no harm.
An interesting group, unconnected it seemed,
although each of them had the same dream.

Men, women and children too,
gradually formed an orderly queue.
Minutes turned to hours... hours to days,
or to those queuing it seemed that way.
Black clouds gathered, no shelter in sight;
they hunkered down for an unsettled night.

In the darkness, a child started to sob;
around midnight a woman really lost the plot.
'This is futile,' she screamed out loud,
as security carried her through the crowd.
Morning came, many had come prepared,
some had brought flasks and food which they shared.

Rest assured, everyone was treated the same,
whether a first timer or a big name.
Anyone complaining that it was "not fair",
just look at those queuing whilst doing their hair,
applying make-up and checking their clothes,
ensuring no bogies protrude from their nose.

After hours of queueing and waiting around,
finally a lad with a megaphone shouted aloud.
Calling out numbers one at a time;
slowly the contestants moved forward in line.
Everyone there had brought some support:
their mother, brother, whoever they thought.

They all had their five minutes of fame;
thousands sent home, two left in the game.
David: 'Go sing your heart out today.'
Nick: 'Go out there, blow them away.'
David mumbled, exhausted, he hardly sung a note.
Nick, energetic and loud, he got the people's vote.

Nick was not the world's greatest singer,
so how on earth did he become the winner?
The contestants all thought their singing had to be the best,
not realising that queuing stamina would actually win the contest.
Nick had trained hard to stand in that queue.
His proudest moment? When Simon smiled, said, 'Well done you.'

Julie

There's a hole in my bucket list

Lists should be on fridges, in bags and in Santa's sack,
not in buckets; there's something wrong with that.
Why write a list of things to do before you die?
Is the list so important... if so, why?

Climb Everest, walk on water, tea with the Queen.
Is everything on your bucket list in your dreams?
Do you think you will enjoy the adrenaline hit?
A quick thrill, each one over as quick as a wink.

Making a cup of tea when you want one,
walking, admiring the rising sun,
meeting your guy without a second thought,
shopping all day, buying more than you ought.

Eating steak without worrying about your meds.
In fact, doing anything without planning ahead.
My list is not in a bucket, as mine is full of holes.
(For this line to rhyme it will have to end in "moles".)

If I sound as if I'm preaching, then I really am not.
Well, maybe I am... but actually I don't care a jot.
What's on your list, or what you keep it in.
Sorry to be rude... but I'd file it in the bin.

Have an adrenaline rush, if that's what you need,
but don't forget the small stuff, the things which help us breathe.
The tiny things that happen, don't let them float away.
Pause, think, listen, enjoy and appreciate each day.

This is Me*

I have Parkinson's
Three small words
Changed my life

This outer shell
Is not me
Do not stare
Do not judge
Do not pity

This outer shell
Is not me
Ignore the mumble
Ignore the stoop
Ignore the shuffle

---

*   This poem is written by me, about me (i.e. by The Parkinality Poet about The Parkinality Poet).

Parkinson's bullies me
Tries to control
I stand up
Take it on
I will overcome

On the outside
I am Parkinson's
On the inside
I am me

I have Parkinson's
Three small words
Changed my life

Finally...

Phyllis and Alfred, the story continues...

Remember that poem about blue and green?
Stating that, 'Together, they should never be seen.'
When I asked, 'Why?'; no-one knew the reason.
Today, anything goes, whatever the season.

So I scheduled a meeting with the powers that be;
which started at nine, and finished around three.
After six hours debating colours today;
"they" relaxed that rule, for just one day.

Meaning a lovely couple could start a new life;
and Phyllis and Alfred became husband and wife.

Please read and watch all things Parkinality, but remember I am an ordinary person dealing with an awful disease. I write to put across my personal feelings and experiences, and hope that other people with Parkinson's Disease (PD) will feel less alone when dealing with such a misunderstood condition. Also to try and explain why I am so unpredictable and unreliable as I show the impact it has on every second of every day, twenty-four seven.

Any information I give is merely my personal opinion. Some of it may turn out to be unintentionally inaccurate, and my experience, opinions and knowledge of living with Parkinson's will inevitably change over time as the disease progresses.

In summary, read, watch, listen to my work and feel free to think (delete as applicable) "that is interesting/boring/irrelevant/just damn odd/worthless/splendid/amazing/fantastic/funny/weird", but do not act on it (please).

For further information:
www.parkinsons.org.uk
www.cureparkinsons.org.uk

Parkinson's UK confidential support line: 0808 800 0303

Parkinality (pa:kin-al-i-tee)

Parkin (son's) (person) ality.
A blend word joining the words Parkinson's and Personality.
I created the word.

The Parkinality Poet is:

A multi-faceted oxymoron with a GSOH.

Her large handbag contains: a blue disabled badge, medication, spare medication, back-up medication, water, disabled bus and train pass, radar key which unlocks ten billion public toilets, an umbrella, and two walking sticks. On a Friday night, you may find her chatting, drinking gin, dancing and getting up to other general malarkey. We have it on good authority that she is not a "pain in the arse".

Previous theatre credits include: *Seaweed, Tree, Lamb* and *The Tin Man* (non-speaking/singing role).

Bits and bobs

I was diagnosed in November 2012, aged forty-four, with early onset Parkinson's Disease (PD). A (currently) incurable, degenerative neurological condition. I try to remain positive and concentrate on what I can do.

I can't cure Parkinson's, but I can raise awareness, in the hope that people will gain an insight and understanding of this unpredictable, debilitative condition, and ultimately that a cure will be found.

Lightning Source UK Ltd.
Milton Keynes UK
UKHW021045300719
347088UK00005B/99/P